GW00420385

Adding
and
Subtracting

Illustrated by
Denise Coble

Addition tables

Learn the addition tables so you can remember them.

1 + 1 =	2
2 + 1 =	3
3 + 1 =	4
4 + 1 =	5
5 + 1 =	6
6 + 1 =	7
7 + 1 =	8
8 + 1 =	9
9 + 1 =	10
10 + 1 =	11
11 + 1 =	12
12 + 1 =	13

1 + 2 =	3
2 + 2 =	4
3 + 2 =	5
4 + 2 =	6
5 + 2 =	7
6 + 2 =	8
7 + 2 =	9
8 + 2 =	10
9 + 2 =	11
10 + 2 =	12
11 + 2 =	13
12 + 2 =	14

1 + 3 =	4
2 + 3 =	5
3 + 3 =	6
4 + 3 =	7
5 + 3 =	8
6 + 3 =	9
7 + 3 =	10
8 + 3 =	11
9 + 3 =	12
10 + 3 =	13
11 + 3 =	14
12 + 3 =	15

1 + 4 =	5
2 + 4 =	6
3 + 4 =	7
4 + 4 =	8
5 + 4 =	9
6 + 4 =	10
7 + 4 =	11
8 + 4 =	12
9 + 4 =	13
10 + 4 =	14
11 + 4 =	15
12 + 4 =	16

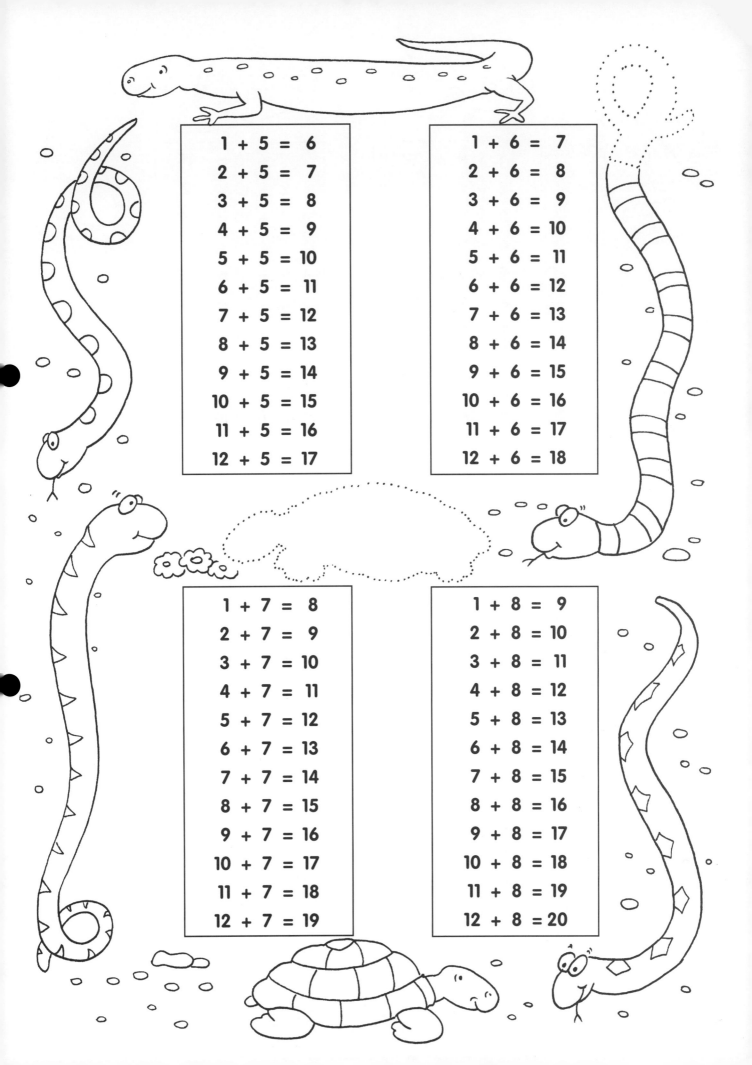

1 + 5 = 6			1 + 6 = 7	
2 + 5 = 7			2 + 6 = 8	
3 + 5 = 8			3 + 6 = 9	
4 + 5 = 9			4 + 6 = 10	
5 + 5 = 10			5 + 6 = 11	
6 + 5 = 11			6 + 6 = 12	
7 + 5 = 12			7 + 6 = 13	
8 + 5 = 13			8 + 6 = 14	
9 + 5 = 14			9 + 6 = 15	
10 + 5 = 15			10 + 6 = 16	
11 + 5 = 16			11 + 6 = 17	
12 + 5 = 17			12 + 6 = 18	

1 + 7 = 8			1 + 8 = 9	
2 + 7 = 9			2 + 8 = 10	
3 + 7 = 10			3 + 8 = 11	
4 + 7 = 11			4 + 8 = 12	
5 + 7 = 12			5 + 8 = 13	
6 + 7 = 13			6 + 8 = 14	
7 + 7 = 14			7 + 8 = 15	
8 + 7 = 15			8 + 8 = 16	
9 + 7 = 16			9 + 8 = 17	
10 + 7 = 17			10 + 8 = 18	
11 + 7 = 18			11 + 8 = 19	
12 + 7 = 19			12 + 8 = 20	

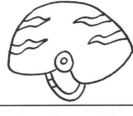
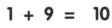

1 + 9 =	10	1 + 10 =	11
2 + 9 =	11	2 + 10 =	12
3 + 9 =	12	3 + 10 =	13
4 + 9 =	13	4 + 10 =	14
5 + 9 =	14	5 + 10 =	15
6 + 9 =	15	6 + 10 =	16
7 + 9 =	16	7 + 10 =	17
8 + 9 =	17	8 + 10 =	18
9 + 9 =	18	9 + 10 =	19
10 + 9 =	19	10 + 10 =	20
11 + 9 =	20	11 + 10 =	21
12 + 9 =	21	12 + 10 =	22

1 + 11 =	12	1 + 12 =	13
2 + 11 =	13	2 + 12 =	14
3 + 11 =	14	3 + 12 =	15
4 + 11 =	15	4 + 12 =	16
5 + 11 =	16	5 + 12 =	17
6 + 11 =	17	6 + 12 =	18
7 + 11 =	18	7 + 12 =	19
8 + 11 =	19	8 + 12 =	20
9 + 11 =	20	9 + 12 =	21
10 + 11 =	21	10 + 12 =	22
11 + 11 =	22	11 + 12 =	23
12 + 11 =	23	12 + 12 =	24

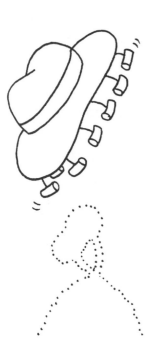

Elephant sums

Do the sums and write the answers in the buckets.

6 + 2 =

4 + 4 =

3 + 7 =

Addition on the farm

Complete the sums.

4 + ☐ = 8

☐ + 7 = 12

7 + ☐ = 14

4 + 3 = ☐

☐ + 6 = 18

9 + ☐ = 16

11 + 5 = ☐

☐ + 8 = 20

8 + 8 = ☐

12 + ☐ = 24

☐ + 8 = 15

10 + 3 = ☐

9 + ☐ = 18

12 + ☐ = 22

11 + 3 = ☐

☐ + 6 = 13

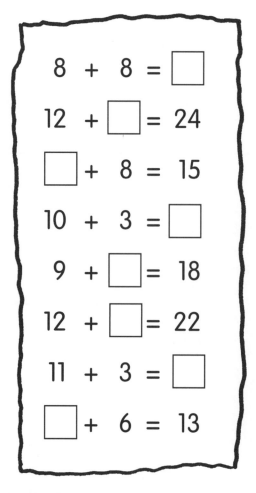

11 + 11 = ☐

7 + ☐ = 19

4 + 3 = ☐

☐ + 11 = 11

8 + ☐ = 21

20 + 3 = ☐

32 + ☐ = 35

18 + 12 = ☐

12 + 12 = ☐

1 + ☐ = 10

☐ + 10 = 20

7 + 9 = ☐

2 + ☐ = 4

8 + 2 = ☐

9 + 7 = ☐

3 + ☐ = 6

Missing numbers

Count the objects to complete the sums.

$$+ = \boxed{}$$

$$\boxed{} + =$$

$$+ \boxed{} =$$

Window sums

Do the sums and write your answers on the doors.

Kite sums

Do the sums by counting the bows on the kites.
When you have an answer, draw the number of bows on the last kite.
The first one has been started for you.

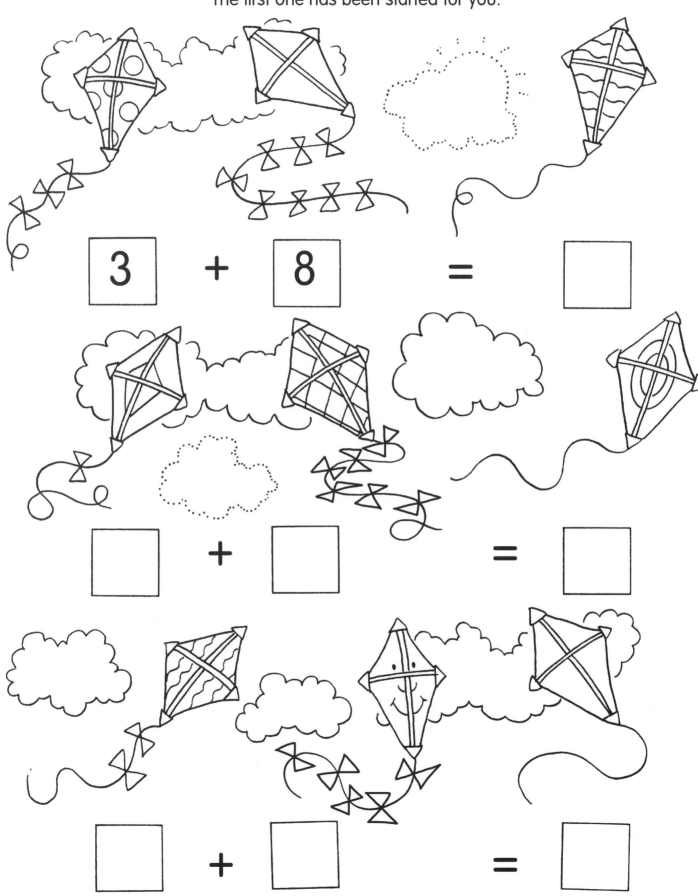

Balloon sums

The answers to the balloon sums are printed on the children's t-shirts.
Draw a line to join each balloon to the correct child.

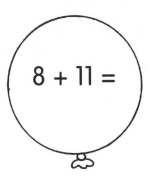

8 + 11 =

9 + 9 =

12 + 10 =

Sums puzzles

Do the sums in the grids by filling in the missing numbers.

	+	8	=	12
+	■	+	■	+
1	+		=	
=	■	=	■	=
	+	11	=	16

11	+		=	20
+	■	+	■	+
	+	2	=	4
=	■	=	■	=
	+	11	=	

Sums crossword

Do the sums. Follow the letters across and down, and write the answers as words in the crossword grid.

a. 6 + 6 =

a. 2 + 0 =

b. 3 + 7 =

c. 9 + 2 =

d. 3 + 1 =

e. 1 + 0 =

f. 2 + 1 =

g. 5 + 3 =

Number lines

Do the sums in the hot-air balloons.
Draw lines to join each answer to its place on the number line.

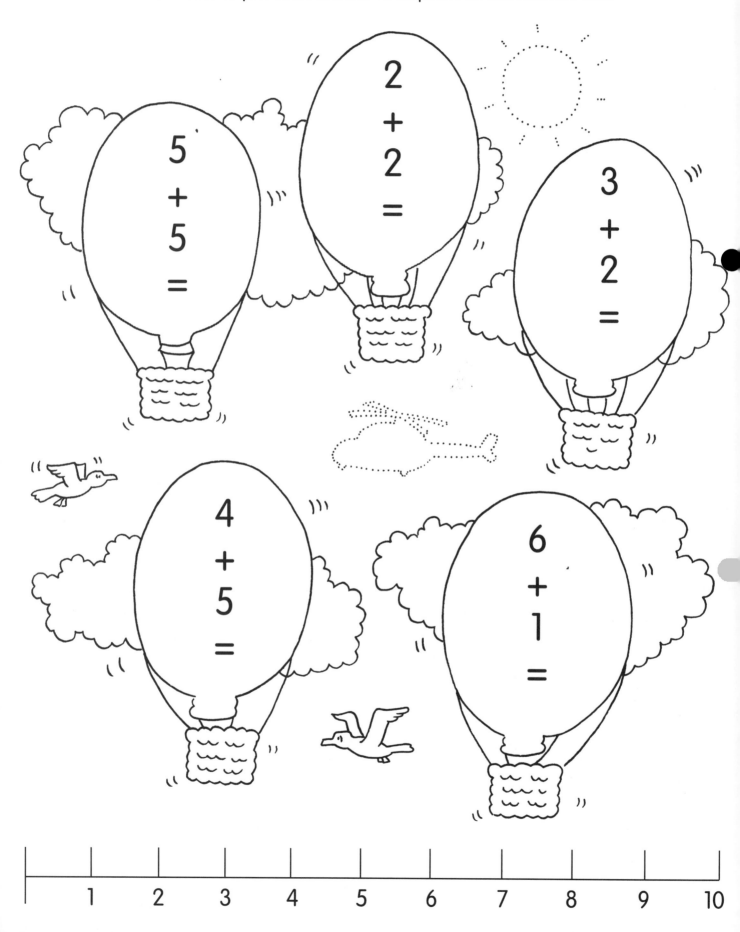

5
+
5
=

2
+
2
=

3
+
2
=

4
+
5
=

6
+
1
=

1   2   3   4   5   6   7   8   9   10

Match the answers

Draw lines to join the sums on the sailboats to their answers on the anchors.

7 + 7 =

8 + 8 =

11 + 11 =

10 + 10 =

16   20   14   22

Addition test

Do the sums and write the answers in the boxes.
Check your answers by looking at the tables.

11 + 2 =

6 + 7 =

10 + 5 =

6 + 9 =

3 + 12 =

2 + 8 =

7 + 6 =

5 + 5 =

8 + 8 =

10 + 3 =

2 + 2 =

4 + 5 =

5 + 8 =

1 + 9 = ☐

3 + 3 = ☐

6 + 6 = ☐

4 + 7 = ☐

9 + 6 = ☐

11 + 11 = ☐

7 + 12 = ☐

3 + 9 = ☐

4 + 2 = ☐

12 + 4 = ☐

8 + 4 = ☐

10 + 6 = ☐

5 + 3 = ☐

Subtraction tables

Learn the subtraction tables so you can remember them.

2 - 1 =	1
3 - 1 =	2
4 - 1 =	3
5 - 1 =	4
6 - 1 =	5
7 - 1 =	6
8 - 1 =	7
9 - 1 =	8
10 - 1 =	9
11 - 1 =	10
12 - 1 =	11
13 - 1 =	12

3 - 2 =	1
4 - 2 =	2
5 - 2 =	3
6 - 2 =	4
7 - 2 =	5
8 - 2 =	6
9 - 2 =	7
10 - 2 =	8
11 - 2 =	9
12 - 2 =	10
13 - 2 =	11
14 - 2 =	12

4 - 3 =	1
5 - 3 =	2
6 - 3 =	3
7 - 3 =	4
8 - 3 =	5
9 - 3 =	6
10 - 3 =	7
11 - 3 =	8
12 - 3 =	9
13 - 3 =	10
14 - 3 =	11
15 - 3 =	12

5 - 4 =	1
6 - 4 =	2
7 - 4 =	3
8 - 4 =	4
9 - 4 =	5
10 - 4 =	6
11 - 4 =	7
12 - 4 =	8
13 - 4 =	9
14 - 4 =	10
15 - 4 =	11
16 - 4 =	12

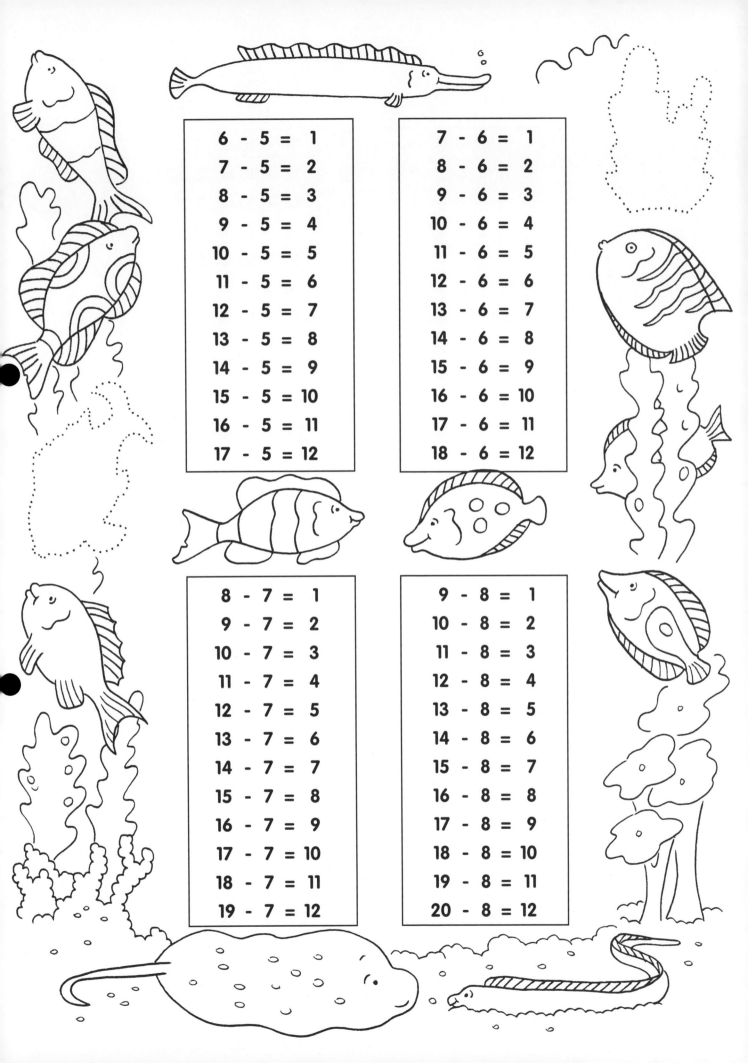

6	-	5	=	1		
7	-	5	=	2		
8	-	5	=	3		
9	-	5	=	4		
10	-	5	=	5		
11	-	5	=	6		
12	-	5	=	7		
13	-	5	=	8		
14	-	5	=	9		
15	-	5	=	10		
16	-	5	=	11		
17	-	5	=	12		

7	-	6	=	1
8	-	6	=	2
9	-	6	=	3
10	-	6	=	4
11	-	6	=	5
12	-	6	=	6
13	-	6	=	7
14	-	6	=	8
15	-	6	=	9
16	-	6	=	10
17	-	6	=	11
18	-	6	=	12

8	-	7	=	1
9	-	7	=	2
10	-	7	=	3
11	-	7	=	4
12	-	7	=	5
13	-	7	=	6
14	-	7	=	7
15	-	7	=	8
16	-	7	=	9
17	-	7	=	10
18	-	7	=	11
19	-	7	=	12

9	-	8	=	1
10	-	8	=	2
11	-	8	=	3
12	-	8	=	4
13	-	8	=	5
14	-	8	=	6
15	-	8	=	7
16	-	8	=	8
17	-	8	=	9
18	-	8	=	10
19	-	8	=	11
20	-	8	=	12

10	- 9	=	1
11	- 9	=	2
12	- 9	=	3
13	- 9	=	4
14	- 9	=	5
15	- 9	=	6
16	- 9	=	7
17	- 9	=	8
18	- 9	=	9
19	- 9	=	10
20	- 9	=	11
21	- 9	=	12

11	- 10	=	1
12	- 10	=	2
13	- 10	=	3
14	- 10	=	4
15	- 10	=	5
16	- 10	=	6
17	- 10	=	7
18	- 10	=	8
19	- 10	=	9
20	- 10	=	10
21	- 10	=	11
22	- 10	=	12

12	- 11	=	1
13	- 11	=	2
14	- 11	=	3
15	- 11	=	4
16	- 11	=	5
17	- 11	=	6
18	- 11	=	7
19	- 11	=	8
20	- 11	=	9
21	- 11	=	10
22	- 11	=	11
23	- 11	=	12

13	- 12	=	1
14	- 12	=	2
15	- 12	=	3
16	- 12	=	4
17	- 12	=	5
18	- 12	=	6
19	- 12	=	7
20	- 12	=	8
21	- 12	=	9
22	- 12	=	10
23	- 12	=	11
24	- 12	=	12

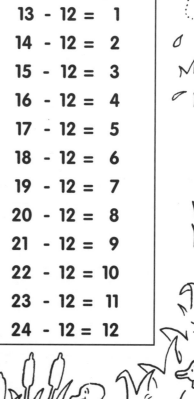

Penguin sums

Do the sums.

6 − 2 =

12 − 10 =

20 − 9 =

Subtraction in space

Complete the sums.

3   – ☐ =   0

☐ –   4   =   8

21 – ☐ =   14

15 –   5   = ☐

☐ –   6   =   18

14 – ☐ =   12

9   –   1   = ☐

☐ –   2   =   16

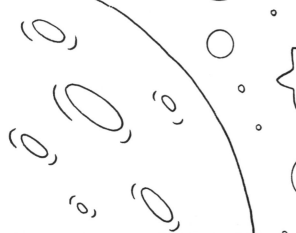

16 –   7   = ☐

24 – ☐ =   24

☐ –   9   =   0

18 – 10 = ☐

22 – ☐ =   11

9   – ☐ =   8

12 –   4   = ☐

☐ –   7   =   15

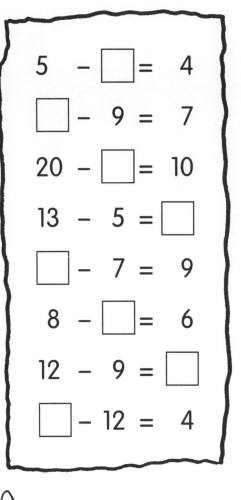

$5 - \boxed{} = 4$

$\boxed{} - 9 = 7$

$20 - \boxed{} = 10$

$13 - 5 = \boxed{}$

$\boxed{} - 7 = 9$

$8 - \boxed{} = 6$

$12 - 9 = \boxed{}$

$\boxed{} - 12 = 4$

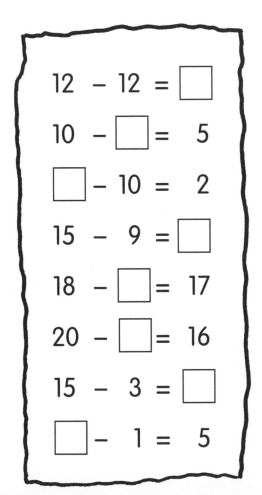

$12 - 12 = \boxed{}$

$10 - \boxed{} = 5$

$\boxed{} - 10 = 2$

$15 - 9 = \boxed{}$

$18 - \boxed{} = 17$

$20 - \boxed{} = 16$

$15 - 3 = \boxed{}$

$\boxed{} - 1 = 5$

Bubble sums

Working upwards from the bubbles on the bottom, do the sums by filling in the missing numbers.

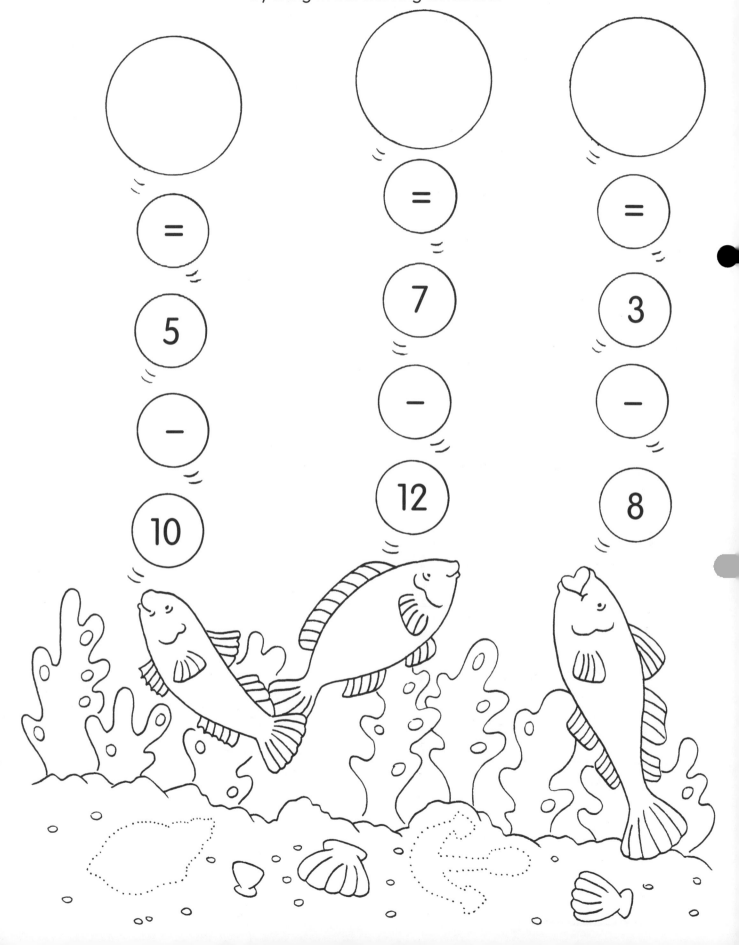

7 = ( ) − 12

9 = 3 − ( )

( ) = 5 − 14

Fun with sums

Solve these problems.

Take 4 bananas away from these monkeys.
How many bananas are left?

If 3 parrots fly away, how many parrots are left?

Colour 6 of the crocodile's teeth. How many teeth are left white?

Two rabbits eat 2 carrots each.
How many carrots are left?

Draw 8 lighted candles on this cake.
If the boy blows out 3 candles,
how many lighted candles are left?

Which is right?

Circle the sums with answers that match
the numbers at the top of each box.

18
10 – 7
33 – 12
15 – 3
27 – 9

40
25 – 5
50 – 10
48 – 6
10 – 5

24
30 – 6
42 – 7
64 – 8
20 – 2

21
45 – 5
21 – 7
30 – 9
10 – 4

10
5 – 5
10 – 1
12 – 2
18 – 7

8
88 – 10
16 – 8
12 – 6
72 – 9

Taking away wordsearch

Do the sums and write the answers in the boxes.
Look for the written answers in the wordsearch grid.
You will find them by reading across and down.
Draw a ring around the words as you find them.

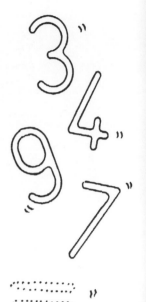

10 − 3 = ☐	15 − 9 = ☐
6 − 2 = ☐	20 − 10 = ☐
12 − 7 = ☐	50 − 20 = ☐
3 − 2 = ☐	8 − 6 = ☐

```
I  E  R  F  O  R  T  B  N
X  K  S  P  S  O  H  J  H
A  S  E  P  C  D  I  V  G
F  I  V  E  Y  T  R  E  X
B  N  E  W  E  R  T  E  N
H  B  N  E  M  K  Y  O  P
T  I  J  F  Y  A  G  S  X
W  D  F  O  N  E  B  I  J
O  Y  T  U  E  X  R  X  N
M  A  I  R  B  F  G  R  E
```

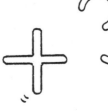

Subtraction test

Do the sums and write the answers in the boxes.
Check your answers by looking at the tables.

8   –   4 = ☐

12   –   2 = ☐

17   –   5 = ☐

20   –   9 = ☐

9   –   1 = ☐

13   –   5 = ☐

24   –   12 = ☐

5   –   5 = ☐

11   –   3 = ☐

20   –   12 = ☐

10   –   4 = ☐

23   –   11 = ☐

13 − 8 = ☐

11 − 1 = ☐

15 − 9 = ☐

3 − 3 = ☐

18 − 6 = ☐

7 − 2 = ☐

16 − 6 = ☐

15 − 5 = ☐

17 − 3 = ☐

7 − 3 = ☐

14 − 12 = ☐

17 − 8 = ☐

6 − 5 = ☐

22 − 10 = ☐

Answers

Elephant sums
6 + 2 = 8   4 + 4 = 8   3 + 7 = 10

Addition on the Farm
4 + 4 = 8   8 + 8 = 16
5 + 7 = 12   12 + 12 = 24
7 + 7 = 14   7 + 8 = 15
4 + 3 = 7   10 + 3 = 13
12 + 6 = 18   9 + 9 = 18
9 + 7 = 16   12 + 10 = 22
11 + 5 = 16   11 + 3 = 14
12 + 8 = 20   7 + 6 = 13

11 + 11 = 22   12 + 12 = 24
7 + 12 = 19   1 + 9 = 10
4 + 3 = 7   10 + 10 = 20
0 + 11 = 11   7 + 9 = 16
8 + 13 = 21   2 + 2 = 4
20 + 3 = 23   8 + 2 = 10
32 + 3 = 35   9 + 7 = 16
18 + 12 = 30   3 + 3 = 6

Missing numbers
6 + 1 = 7   5 + 4 = 9   3 + 2 = 5

Window sums
3 + 12 = 15   5 + 5 = 10   9 + 6 = 15

Kite sums
3 + 8 = 11   1 + 6 = 7   2 + 5 = 7

Balloon sums
8 + 11 = 19   9 + 9 = 18   12 + 10 = 22

Sums puzzles

4	+	8	=	12
+	■	+	■	+
1	+	3	=	4
=	■	=	■	=
5	+	11	=	16

11	+	9	=	20
+	■	+	■	+
2	+	2	=	4
=	■	=	■	=
13	+	11	=	24

Sums crossword
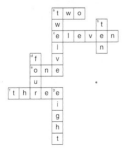

Number lines
5 + 5 = 10   2 + 2 = 4   3 + 2 = 5
4 + 5 = 9   6 + 1 = 7

Match the answers
7 + 7 = 14   8 + 8 = 16
11 + 11 = 22   10 + 10 = 20

Penguin sums
6 - 2 = 4   12 - 10 = 2   20 - 9 = 11

Subtractions in Space
3 – 3 = 0   16 – 7 = 9
12 – 4 = 8   24 – 0 = 24
21 – 7 = 14   9 – 9 = 0
15 – 5 = 10   18 – 10 = 8
24 – 6 = 18   22 – 11 = 11
14 – 2 = 12   9 – 1 = 8
9 – 1 = 8   12 – 4 = 8
18 – 2 = 16   22 – 7 = 15

5 – 1 = 4   12 – 12 = 0
16 – 9 = 7   10 – 5 = 5
20 – 10 = 10   12 – 10 = 2
13 – 5 = 8   15 – 9 = 6
16 – 7 = 9   18 – 1 = 17
8 – 2 = 6   20 – 4 = 16
12 – 9 = 3   15 – 3 = 12
16 – 12 = 4   6 – 1 = 5

Bubble sums
10 - 5 = 5   12 - 7 = 5   8 - 3 = 5
12 - 5 = 7   12 - 3 = 9   14 - 5 = 9

Fun with sums
2 bananas are left   2 carrots are left
4 parrots are left   5 candles are left
5 teeth are left white

Which is right?
27 - 9 = 18   50 - 10 = 40   30 - 6 = 24
30 - 9 = 21   12 - 2 = 10   16 - 8 = 8

Taking away wordsearch

Help with Homework

Adding and Subtracting

The workbooks and pads in the **Help with Homework** series have been compiled to give children confidence with their school work. The exercises are fun to do and are suitable for children 6 – 8 years old.

It is recommended that an adult spends time with a child while doing any kind of school practice, to give encouragement and guidance. Concentration levels in children vary, so do not always expect your child to be able to complete an exercise in one session.

As well as the benefit of practising school work at home, the added activity of finding stickers and putting them in place helps with recognition and comprehension skills.

Create a file of your child's work by filing the books in a standard two-ring binder.

Titles in this series:

5 – 7 years	6 – 8 years
(Key stage 1)	(Key stage 2)
Maths	Adding and Subtracting
Adding	Multiplying and Dividing
Subtracting	Mental Maths
Tell the Time	Times Tables
Phonics	Reading and Writing
Handwriting	Handwriting
Spelling	Spelling
Reading and Writing	More Spelling

www.autumnpublishing.co.uk

Illustrated by Denise Coble
© 2002 Autumn Publishing
This edition published in 2008 by Autumn Publishing
A division of Bonnier Media Ltd,
Chichester, West Sussex, PO20 7EQ, UK.

Printed in Spain

This product is not suitable for children under 36 months, due to small parts.

£2.50 C€

001-08

ISBN-13: 978-1-85997-636-4
ISBN-10: 1-85997-636-0

9 781859 976364